Acknowledgments

With huge thanks to my husband who has lovingly illustrated this book. Your talent (and patience) knows no bounds.
To my beautiful children for being my endless source of joy and inspiration.
To Suzy, for believing in me when I didn't and for showing me the true meaning of unconditional positive regard, without which I would have never been brave enough to even dream that I could.
Special thanks to Marius for inspiring me and for pushing me to put my ideas onto the page.

Dear Reader,

We use the term 'ADHD' as if everyone ought to know what it is. After my son was diagnosed, I realised that I actually had no idea what it really meant. In fact, all I could be certain of was that I had been apologising for my son's behaviour, several times a week, every week for the past decade.

When my son asked me "How poorly am I Mum?" I realised that I talked about ADHD to him as if I expected him to just know what it was, and now that we were discussing medication, he genuinely thought he was poorly, and that's where the idea of this book came from. I couldn't find anything to support him to celebrate himself and his ADHD without him feeling like there was something fundamentally wrong with him.

His feedback is that he wished he had this book when he was younger, he wished the other children in his class had this book when he was younger, and their parents were excluding him from birthday parties, and telling their kids not to play with him because he was "naughty". Indeed, he is still rebuilding his self-esteem having spent years feeling misunderstood.

This book is a gift from us to any child who feels misunderstood because they find it tricky to behave as people expect them to, whether that's down to ADHD or not. Every single one of you has an amazing engine, and with patience and practice you are going to learn to drive it and go to some of the most amazing places.

So keep going!

Laila Oliver

To my first love, Cyrus.
That amazing engine of yours has certainly kept me on my toes,
but I wouldn't have you any other way.

Robbie and his Amazing Engine

by Laila Oliver

Illustrated by Luke Oliver

Robbie is super *quick!*
Robbie is super COOL!
Robbie is zooming SUPER FAST,
all the way to school.

Robbie is very clever.
Robbie is very **kind.**
But sometimes Robbie can go so *fast*
That he leaves his focus behind

Robbie ***doesn't mean it***,
Robbie feels really **SAD**,
Robbie **doesn't know why** he does things
That make other people so **MAD**!

Robbie gets to **school**
He's **READY** to start the day
He's answered all the questions *already!*
And now he wants to **PLAY**

Robbie just **cannot sit still**
He's **raring** for the next task
He finds it so **HARD TO SIT** and wait
When his engine is built to go *fast*

Robbie *looks around* him,
He **NEEDS** to find something to do,
"**WHY** is everyone taking so long**?!**

"I know! Let's *shake things up* with a ...."

VROOOOOM!

The school has called Mum who is **cross**,
Robbie **did not mean** to do wrong
"I finished my work and needed something to DO,
The others were just taking too *looooong*!"

Robbie feels **ANGRY** and **SAD**,
He **kicks out** on the way to the hall,
He has to miss playtime *again*,
He just **HATES HIS LIFE** and this school!!

But then - who is this smiling, and *why?*
"I thought **everyone thinks I am bad**"

"No" says the man,
"MY ENGINE'S THE SAME
and I was like you, when I was a lad."

"Robbie - your engine's *AMAZING!*"
"You mean - there's **NOTHING WRONG** with me?"
"It's just **tricky to learn** how to drive it
But *you'll get there* - just **wait and see!** "

"Come and see all of the *greats*
Who have engines just as **quick**

Most others would **LOVE** an

ENGINE LIKE THAT

It's a gift to be so *shiny and slick*"

Your engine's what **MAKES YOU** "Robbie"
You are **imaginative,** WITTY and *smart*
Your engine helps you think ***outside of the box***,
So **dear child** try not to lose heart"

"But then why am I **always** in trouble?
It does **NOT** feel very nice!"

"You **can learn** to apply the brakes, my dear
You **will learn** to stop and think twice"

"It will take some *practice* and *patience*
You may need some *help* and some **TIME**
But with the right oil and **learning to pause**
YOU ARE GOING TO BE JUST FINE "

So here is Robbie's **ROADMAP**,
He has already tried lots of ways,
Some worked and others not so much
But as the wise chap says...

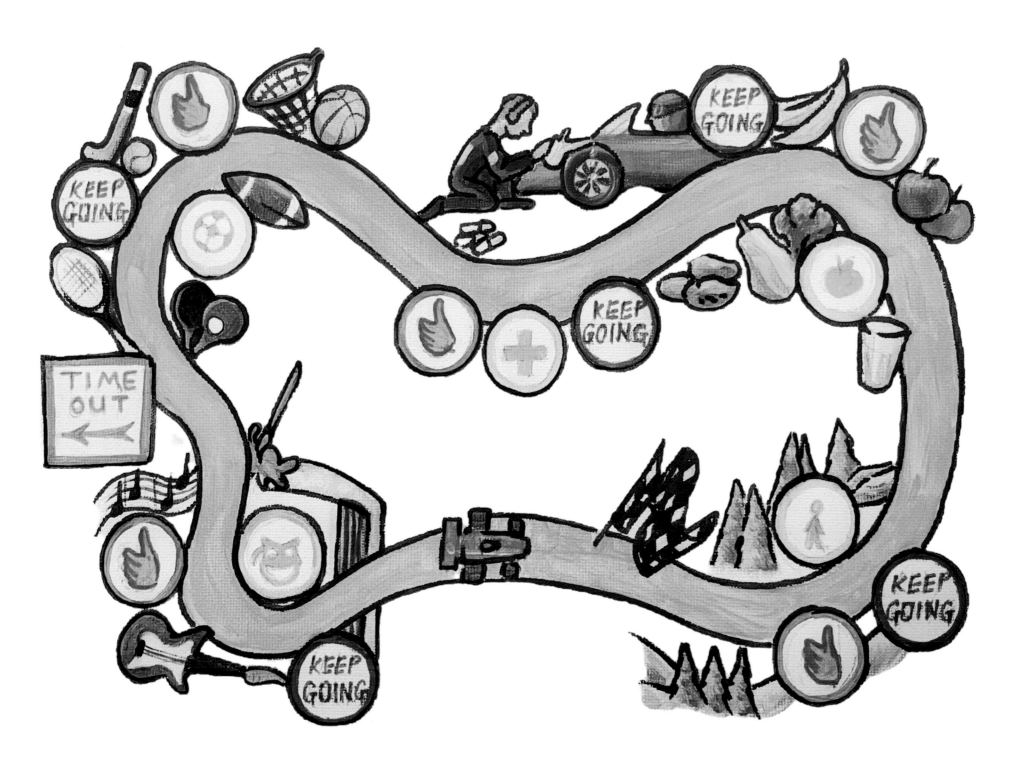

"It will take some *practice* and *patience*,
He needs a little more **help** and some **TIME**,
But as he **keeps persevering**,
HE IS GOING TO BE JUST FINE "

Robbie is super *quick!*
Robbie is super COOL!
Robbie is zooming SUPER FAST,
all the way to school.

Robbie is super clever.
Robbie is super **kind.**
Robbie has **tried** so many things
To help him slow his **AMAZING** mind

Robbie **sees** the crossing
Robbie **APPLIES** the brakes
He **SKIDS AND SWERVES** and *spins around*
But alas it was **STILL TOO LATE**...

Robbie is very **sad**,
He feels extremely **CROSS** and upset,
But to his *surprise* no one else is cross
Because they could see that he TRIED HIS BEST,

"We do not expect you to be **perfect**
You are still just a person like me
Everyone does something wrong sometimes
That's the way we **learn**, you see!"

"Remember,
there is NOTHING WRONG with your engine
And once you have got the knack
People will **gasp with wonder**,
As you *skilfully whizz round* the track."

The end.

(although — the journey really has only just begun...)

About the author

Laila Oliver is a social worker with 15 years of dedicated service in children's social care. Her passion lies in trauma-informed, strengths based practice, where she has focussed her interests. As a mother of three herself, Laila understands the complexities of parenting, particularly with a child diagnosed with ADHD. Her firsthand experience in managing the challenges of impulsive behaviour, both in her professional and personal experience inspired her to write this book. Within the story, Laila uses her unique insight to emphasise the profound importance of unconditional positive regard and compassion when working with challenging behaviours and children.

BV - #0085 - 070224 - C26 - 210/297/3 - PB - 9781836021292 - Gloss Lamination